D1405037

God Made Light

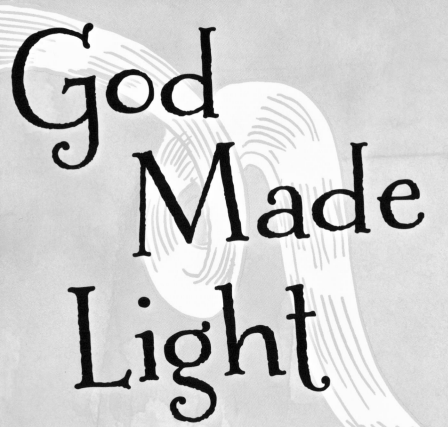

Written by
Matthew Paul Turner

Illustrated by
Matthew Paul Mewhorter

"Let there be light!"

That's what God said.
And light began shining
and then started to spread.

In flickers and flashes,
in spills and in splashes,
shine began shining across
nothing but blackness.

Light glared and glimmered.
It flared and sparked.
And wherever light shined,
dark stopped being dark.

In the beginning
space became bright
'cause God doused it with
twinkles of yellowy white;

Brilliant stars gleaming,
swirls of light streaming
against the pitch black—a galaxy beaming.

When God
said, "Light!"
the universe lit up,
a dazzling display
of big shiny stuff.

And all that light,
every bright golden hue—
did you know that God put that
same light inside you?

Now, God made the sun
to light up our days,
to cover our planet with life-filled rays,
to make summers warm
and winters not too cold,

To help flowers bloom and
turn wheat fields to gold,
to burst in the morning
at the first crack of dawn,
to rise up slowly and beam across lawns.

And when
the sun shines,
here's what you should do:
Go run and have fun; play a game, maybe two.

Go skipping or flipping
or down a slide slipping!
Or if it's too hot, in a pool
you go dipping.

Dance in the grass.
Go climbing in trees.

Build castles
with sand.
Face the wind—
feel its breeze!

And once in a while
when the playing is done,
look up in the sky
and thank God for the sun.

And when the sun sets
and a day ends too soon,
remember God's light always
shines inside you.

So wave goodbye to the sun—
you'll see it again soon.

Then shout a friendly, "Hello!" to the beautiful moon.

Yes, the moon God made
to brighten the sky's night,
to reflect the sun's shine,
to be the night sky's light.

But beneath a dark sky,
there are things you can do;
just bring mommy or daddy
and a flashlight or two.

Raise a tent and go camping
or through the woods stamping,
romping and stomping
on paths made for tramping.

Catch fireflies in jars.
Go gazing at stars.
Try counting and seeing
how many there are.

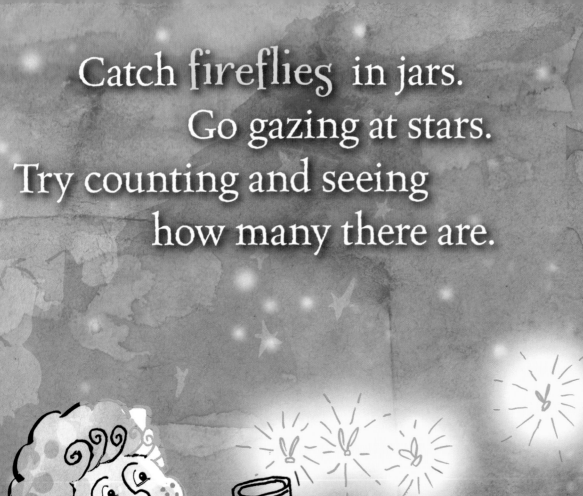

Sing songs 'round campfires.
Make marshmallow s'mores.

Let Grandpa
tell stories.
Wage flashlight
wars!

And if you ever feel scared
in the darkness of night,
remember the shadows are no match
for God's light.

Climb into bed.
Sleep soundly and dream
'cause inside of you God's bright
light is agleam.

'Cause you're just like the sun
and the moon in the sky.
You're as lustrous as twinkles
that dazzle the eye.

You're as splendid as lightning
when it flashes so bright
'cause on the day you were born,
God said, "Let there be light!"

So beam like the sun;
glimmer like a star.
And wherever *you* go,
dark will stop being dark.

Shimmer and shine; be a beacon so bright—
'cause when God made
you, child, God
made light.

For Elias and Adeline, may God's light always shine on you.

Learn more about the author Matthew Paul Turner, the illustrator Matthew Paul Mewhorter, and find other God Made Light products on GodMadeLight.com.

Matthew Paul Turner
P.O. Box 210072
Nashville, TN 37221

ISBN 978-1-63068-632-1
1. Stories in rhyme 2. Children's picture book 3. Bible stories

This book was illustrated by Matthew Paul Mewhorter and designed by Trent Design, Inc. The artwork was created on Strathmore Bristol plate surface paper, and drawn using Pentel black Brush Pen, Pentel Stylos pen, and Pentel Technica pen. The artwork was digitally colored in Adobe Photoshop and Adobe Illustrator.